Retold by

N. J. Dawood

Ali Baba and
the Forty Thieves

PENGUIN BOOKS

PENGUIN BOOKS

Published by the Penguin Group
Penguin Books Ltd, 27 Wrights Lane, London w8 5tz, England
Penguin Books USA Inc., 375 Hudson Street, New York, New York 10014, USA
Penguin Books Australia Ltd, Ringwood, Victoria, Australia
Penguin Books Canada Ltd, 10 Alcorn Avenue, Toronto, Ontario, Canada m4v 3b2
Penguin Books (NZ) Ltd, 182–190 Wairau Road, Auckland 10, New Zealand

Penguin Books Ltd, Registered Offices: Harmondsworth, Middlesex, England

The translations of these stories were first published in *Sindbad the Sailor and Other*
***Tales from The Arabian Nights* in the USA by Doubleday & Company Inc. 1978**
Published in Great Britain in Puffin Books 1989

This collection published in Penguin Books 1996
1 3 5 7 9 10 8 6 4 2

This collection copyright © N. J. Dawood, 1978
All rights reserved

Set in 12.5/13.5pt Bembo Monotype
Typeset by Datix International Limited, Bungay, Suffolk
Printed in England by Clays Ltd, St Ives plc

Contents

Ali Baba and the Forty Thieves

LONG ago there lived in a city of Persia two brothers whose names were Kassim and Ali Baba.

Though born of the same parents and brought up in the same home, their characters were quite different. Kassim, the elder, was arrogant, shrewd, and greedy, while Ali Baba was unassuming, kind-hearted, and content with his situation. When their father died, they divided all he had between them and started life on an equal footing, but while Kassim married a rich wife and became the owner of a thriving shop in the city's main bazaar, Ali Baba took to wife the daughter of a humble family, and earned a modest living by cutting wood in the forest and selling it in the town.

Ali Baba lived frugally and wisely with his wife, saving as much as his earnings would allow, so that in a few months he was able to buy three donkeys. Every day he would lead his donkeys to the forest and bring them back laden with firewood.

1

One day, while working at the edge of a far thicket, with his donkeys grazing peacefully near by, he heard the clatter of galloping hoofs in the distance and saw a great cloud of dust approaching. Curious to find out the cause of the commotion, he climbed cautiously into a tall tree that stood on a hillside, giving a clear view of the adjacent plain. From his hiding place he saw a troop of fierce-looking armed horsemen riding toward him. He counted forty of them, and guessed from their appearance and demeanor – their fiery eyes, their black, pointed beards, and the weapons they carried – that they were a band of robbers.

When they came under the tree, the forty thieves dismounted at a signal from the captain and started removing their saddlebags. They carried their loads to a great rock at the bottom of the hill; then the captain went up to the rock and in a loud voice cried, 'Open, Sesame!'

Ali Baba was astonished to notice that, at the mention of this word – the name of a cereal commonly grown in Persia – a hidden door in the rock swung wide open. The entire band of robbers filed in. In a few moments they emerged, carrying their now-empty saddlebags in their hands, and the captain cried, 'Close, Sesame!' The rock at once shut behind them, and no one could have guessed there was any opening in that solid surface.

As soon as the robbers had mounted and ridden off, Ali Baba climbed down from the tree and went up to the mysterious rock. Finding the surface as smooth and solid as before, he marveled at the magic that had forced it open.

'What priceless treasures must lie within it!' he reflected, and, remembering the captain's words, decided to utter them himself and see what would happen.

'Open, Sesame!' he shouted.

The rock opened, just as it had done before, and Ali Baba walked in. Being a good Moslem, he murmured as he entered, 'In the name of Allah, the Compassionate, the Merciful!' He found himself in a huge cave piled up with rich ornaments, chests brimful with gold and silver coins, and great bags bursting with precious 3 stones — which must have taken hundreds of years to accumulate. As he scanned the vast treasures, Ali Baba realized that the cave was the secret storehouse of countless generations of thieves and highwaymen.

Carefully choosing six bags of gold, he loaded them on his donkeys and covered them with brushwood to hide them. Then he cried aloud, 'Close, Sesame!' and in a twinkling the door slid to behind him, leaving not a trace on the rock's outer surface.

When Ali Baba arrived home and his wife saw him unload the bags of gold, she was seized with shame and fear.

'Good husband,' she said, 'do not tell me you have earned all this gold by cutting wood in the forest. Bad luck is sure to enter our humble house if we keep such ill-gotten gains here.'

'Fear nothing, I am no thief,' Ali Baba quickly interrupted. 'Rather rejoice, for it was Allah who guided my footsteps in the forest this morning.' And he told her of his adventure and how he had found the gold in the robbers' hide-out.

When she heard the story, the poor woman

was filled with relief and joy. She squatted before the pile of gold that her husband had poured out of the bags and tried to value the incalculable coins.

'Don't try to count them,' said Ali Baba with a laugh. 'It would take you days to do that. Get up now and help me dig a ditch in the kitchen where we can hide them. To leave them here would only rouse the suspicions of our neighbors.'

But his wife wanted to know exactly how rich they were. 'If I cannot count them,' she said, 'I must at least weigh or measure them. I will go and borrow a measure from your brother Kassim's house, and then I can measure the gold while you dig the hole.'

She went over to Kassim's house across the lane and begged his wife to lend her a measure.

'You can have one,' her sister-in-law replied. But she wondered at the same time why Ali Baba should need a measure when he was so poor that he could buy only a day's supply of wheat at a time. So the cunning woman, curious to know what kind of grain he was measuring, 5 devised a trick; she rubbed the bottom of the wooden vessel with some fat.

Ali Baba's wife quickly returned home and, after measuring out the gold, carried the measure back to Kassim's wife, not knowing that a gold piece had stuck to the fat at the bottom.

'What have we here?' cried Kassim's wife as soon as her kinswoman had left her. 'So Ali Baba is now too rich to count his gold and has to measure it!'

Jealousy gripped her soul. She sent a servant to fetch her husband from his shop, and told him the story in a fit of rage. 'We cannot let the matter rest at that,' she screamed. 'You must go now and force that wretched brother of yours to reveal to you the source of his riches!'

Instead of being pleased that his brother was no longer a poor man, Kassim, too, was overwhelmed with envy. His heart burning with spite, he immediately went over to Ali Baba's house.

'How is it that you dare to deceive us so?' he cried. 'You go on pretending to be penniless and 6 humble, when you have so much gold that you cannot even count it. Tell me this moment how you came by it, or I will denounce you as an impostor and a thief!'

He showed his brother the gold piece still smeared with fat, and Ali Baba, seeing at once how his secret had been discovered, confided to Kassim the whole story and begged him to keep quiet about it.

There and then, the greedy Kassim resolved to take possession of the treasure for himself alone. He left his brother and quickly returned home, his head buzzing with a thousand plans.

Early next morning he set out with ten donkeys to find the cave that Ali Baba had described. When he came to the rock under the tree, he stretched out his arms toward it and shouted, 'Open, Sesame!' And exactly as his brother had told him, the rock opened to let him in. He tied his donkeys to some trees, entered the cave, then closed the rock behind him with the magic words.

Kassim was dumbfounded at the sight of the robbers' treasure, and his very soul was stirred by the prospect of caravan after caravan carrying the riches home. He gathered twenty of the largest sacks of gold and jewels and dragged them to the entrance. Then he tried to remember the magic words. 'Open, Barley!' he cried.

But the rock did not open.

The miserable Kassim, preoccupied with the acquisition of so much gold, had completely forgotten the all-powerful words. Again and again he shouted, 'Open, Wheat! Open, Barley! Open, Beans!' to the door, which obeyed no sound but 'Open, Sesame!'

And as he stood shaking with rage and terror before the impenetrable rock, the forty thieves came riding up to the cave.

When they saw the ten donkeys tethered near the entrance they leaped down from their horses and scattered around in search of the intruder, brandishing their swords and yelling angry curses. Then the captain pointed toward the rock and pronounced the two words that rent it asunder. The robbers were enraged to find a stranger in their treasure house. They swooped upon Kassim with their swords and hacked him into 8 six pieces, then hung the pieces just inside the cave as a lesson and a warning to other would-be intruders.

When night came and Kassim did not return home, his wife grew very anxious. She went over to Ali Baba's house and begged him to go and look for her husband. Fearing that the worst might have happened, Ali Baba took his three donkeys and rode off at sunrise to the robbers' cave.

With a trembling voice he cried, 'Open, Sesame!' and when the rock opened, he walked in. He was stricken with grief at the sight of Kassim's body cut in pieces. With a heavy heart he took down the pieces and put them carefully together into two empty sacks, which he loaded onto one of his donkeys. He loaded the other two beasts with more sacks of gold, then commanded the rocky door to shut and led his donkeys home.

On reaching the courtyard of his house, he knocked at the door, and it was opened by the slave Marjanah, who was the cleverest and most faithful of his servants.

'Marjanah, my girl,' said Ali Baba, 'today you

can give us proof of your ingenuity and wisdom. Your master's brother has been killed by robbers and cut into pieces, but no one must know about it. Think of some way by which we can bury him without arousing any suspicions.'

Then he went to his brother's house and broke the bad news to Kassim's wife.

'Do not grieve, dear sister,' he said. 'Allah has given me more riches than I can use. Come and live in our house, and share everything with us. But no one must know our secret.'

They unloaded the pieces of Kassim's body, and discreetly told the neighbors that he had died suddenly in his sleep.

Then Marjanah went to the shop of an old cobbler in another part of the town where she was quite unknown.

'We want you to do a little sewing,' she said. 'Bring your needles and thread with you. Your work must be secret, and I must blindfold you and lead you to the house.'

At first the old cobbler refused, but when Mar-
10 janah slipped a piece of gold into his hand, he

allowed himself to be led along the streets and down into the cellar of Ali Baba's house. There she showed him the pieces of Kassim's body, slipped another gold coin into his hand, and bade him sew them together, adding, 'If you work quickly you shall have two more pieces of gold.'

The old man set to work at once and sewed the parts so neatly that no one would see the stitching. She led him back blindfolded to his shop, and returned home to make arrangements for Kassim's funeral. Thus Kassim was buried according to the customary rites, and no one outside the household had the slightest suspicion of the way he had met his death.

When the forty thieves paid their next visit to the cave they were dismayed to find no sign of Kassim's body.

'My men,' the captain said, 'it is clear that someone else knows our secret. We must find out at once who the accomplice of the man we killed is.'

Calling one of the robbers, he said to him, 'Disguise yourself as a holy dervish. Go into the town and find out the identity of the man whose body we cut to pieces.'

Just before sunrise next morning the robber entered the town, and the first shop he saw open was the old cobbler's. He greeted the old man, praised his wares, and engaged him in a friendly conversation.

'I see, good sir, that you begin work before sunrise,' he began. 'Your eyes must be very good indeed to see so well in the gray light of dawn.'

'Allah be praised, good dervish,' replied the cobbler. 'I can still thread a needle at the first attempt. Why, only yesterday I sewed together the parts of a man's body in a dark cellar without a light.'

'Indeed,' said the robber, 'and who might the man be?'

'That I cannot tell,' the cobbler replied, 'for I was blindfolded and led to the place by an impudent girl, and brought back the same way.'

The robber slipped a gold coin into the cobbler's hand.

'I would like nothing better,' he said, 'than to 12 be taken myself to that house. I will blindfold you, and you can grope your way along the same route you followed yesterday. Take me there and you shall have more gold.'

The cobbler allowed his eyes to be bandaged and, holding on to the robber's sleeve, felt his way slowly to Ali Baba's house; and there he stopped.

'This is most certainly the place,' he cried.

The robber was overjoyed at the discovery. He removed the old man's bandage, slipped a second gold piece into his hand, and sent him back to his shop. Then he took a piece of chalk out of his pocket and with it marked the door of Ali Baba's house. This done, he returned with all possible speed to the forest and told his captain the good news.

When, soon afterward, honest Marjanah went to do the shopping, she noticed the white mark upon the door and thought to herself, 'This is an evil sign, the work of an enemy plotting my master's ruin.'

So she fetched a piece of chalk and made the same mark on the doors of all the houses in the street.

Next morning the thieves came one by one into the town to break into the house their spy had marked for them, and to avenge themselves on everyone who lived in it. But when the robber led them into the street, they were confounded to see that all the doors were marked in the same way, so that it was impossible to tell which was the house they sought. The angry captain sent them back to the forest, with orders to put the foolish spy to death.

'It seems that I shall have to go myself,' said the robber chief.

So next day he rode into the city in disguise and went straight to the old cobbler, who led him to Ali Baba's house. But the captain did not mark the door this time. He gazed long and carefully at it until its very image was engraved upon his memory, and then he returned to the forest.

He called the thieves together and said to them, 'I know the house for certain now. To-morrow we shall be avenged. All I require you to do is to bring me thirty-nine earthenware jars, each large enough to contain a full-grown man.

One of them must be filled with cooking oil, the rest must be empty.'

The thieves, who always obeyed the captain, rode off at once to the market place and returned with thirty-nine large jars. One of these jars they filled with oil, and in each of the others a robber hid himself, on the captain's orders. The chief armed each with a dagger and club, and covered the mouth of each vessel with a muslin cloth, so that the men inside would be hidden and yet breathe freely. Then he loaded his men's horses with the jars, linked the animals together, and drove them toward the city.

When he came to Ali Baba's house, he found the woodcutter seated on his threshold, enjoying the cool evening air.

'Peace be to you, my master,' said the captain with a low bow. 'I am an oil merchant and have been traveling the road these three days. I am a stranger in this city and do not know where to pass the night. I pray that you will give hospitality, for myself and my horses, in the courtyard of your house.'

'You are most welcome, sir,' said Ali Baba kindly.

He took his guest by the hand and led him into his house. Then he ordered Marjanah to help with the unloading of the jars, to feed the horses, and to prepare a hot meal for the stranger.

Now, the captain had told his men that when he threw a pebble into the jars they were to come out of the jars and join him. So they crouched there, patiently waiting for the signal.

Meanwhile, Marjanah, who was busily cooking the dinner in the kitchen, found her lamp going out for lack of oil.

'We surely cannot complain of being short of oil,' she said to herself, 'when there are thirty-nine jars full of it in the courtyard. I will go and take a little from one of them.'

She took her lamp and went to fill it, but as she touched the first jar a voice whispered, 'Is it time?'

The quick-witted Marjanah guessed at once

what was afoot, and instead of screaming with

fright, whispered back in as deep a voice as she could, 'Not yet!'

As she approached the jars in turn, from each came the same question, and to each she gave the same answer, until she came to the last jar, which she found was in fact filled with oil. After taking what she needed, she returned to the kitchen, lit the lamp, and set to work upon a plan to save her master.

From the last jar she quickly filled a great caldron with oil and set it over the fire to boil. Then she poured the boiling oil into those of the jars in which the thieves were hidden and killed them all.

After dinner the captain of the robbers retired to bed, and at midnight, seeing no light and hearing no sound, he threw his pebble into the yard. But there was no answer, and not one robber appeared.

'The dogs have gone to sleep,' he muttered.

When he ran down to the courtyard and looked into the jars, he found that all his men were dead. Realizing that his plan was discovered and that he himself might be in danger of his life, 17 he leaped over the courtyard wall and fled. On and on he ran until he reached the treasure cave, where he sat brooding over the calamitous end of his followers.

Next morning, Marjanah took Ali Baba into the courtyard and showed him the jars. He recoiled in horror when he looked into the first and saw a dead man inside, but the girl quickly told him the whole story. Now he rejoiced to hear that all the robbers were dead and was deeply thankful to Marjanah.

'From this moment,' he declared, 'you are no longer a slave, but our own beloved daughter.'

Ali Baba buried the thieves' bodies in a great pit and lived in peace and contentment with his family for many months.

One day, Ali Baba's oldest son, who by now had become a rich merchant with a shop of his own, said to his father, 'I do not know how to repay my neighbor, the merchant Husain, for all the kindness he has shown me since he took the shop next door to mine. I should much like to invite him to our house and give a feast in his honor.'

'Invite him, by all means,' Ali Baba replied. 'He will be most welcome.'

But when the merchant arrived, he said to Ali Baba, 'You do me great honor in inviting me to your house, but alas, I cannot eat with you. I have made a vow never to taste salt or eat any meat flavored with it.'

'That is no difficult matter,' Ali Baba cried. 'I will give orders that no salt be put into our food tonight.' And he hurried into the kitchen to tell Marjanah that she should use no salt in the cooking.

This odd request aroused the girl's suspicions and she looked closely at the guest when she carried the dishes in. Her horror knew no bounds when she recognized the captain of the robbers and saw that he had a dagger hidden in the folds of his robe.

'So that's why the villain would not eat salt with the man he intends to kill,' she thought.

When the meal was over, Marjanah entered the room, and Ali Baba and his son were astonished to see the dress she had put on; it was that of a dancer. Holding a dagger in one hand, she 19 danced gracefully, to the delight of all the company, particularly that of the disguised robber, who took out his purse to throw a gold coin to her. As he bent forward she flung herself upon him and plunged her dagger into his heart.

'What have you done, you foolish girl!' Ali Baba exclaimed, aghast at the deed.

'You have killed the kind old man!' cried the son.

'I have saved your lives!' Marjanah cried. And she showed them the dagger hidden in the visitor's robe, and then told them who he really was and how she had found him out.

When Ali Baba realized that the girl had saved him yet once more, he took her into his arms and said, 'You shall marry my son and become in all truth my daughter; for you have truly earned this reward.'

And so Marjanah was wedded to Ali Baba's son, amid great rejoicing.

For a long time, Ali Baba kept away from the robbers' cave, but when one year had passed he went there with his son and Marjanah. He found the little path that led up to the rock overgrown with long grass, with not a sign of man or beast, and knew that the cave was now perfectly safe. He flung out his arms toward the rock, crying, 'Open, Sesame!' and once again the door opened, revealing the secret treasure untouched since the death of the robbers.

So Ali Baba became the richest and most influential man of his time, and lived in tranquillity and joy until the end of his life.

The Tale of the Hunchback

ONCE upon a time, in the city of Basra, a tailor was taking an evening walk with his wife when they met a sprightly little hunchback who was merrily singing and clashing a tambourine. His merriment was so infectious that it banished grief and sorrow and every other care. The couple were so amused by the hunchback that they invited him to spend the evening with them as their guest. He accepted, and when they had reached home the tailor hurried out to the market place, where he bought some fried fish, bread, and lemons, and honey for dessert.

The three sat down to a hilarious meal. Being fond of practical jokes, the tailor's wife crammed a large piece of fish into the hunchback's mouth and forced him to swallow it. But, as fate would have it, the fish concealed a large and sharp bone that stuck in his throat and choked him. When they examined him they found, to their horror, that the hunchback was dead.

The tailor lifted up his hands and exclaimed,

'There is no strength or power save in Allah! Alas that this man should have met his death at our hands, and in this fashion!'

'Crying will not help us,' said his wife. 'We must do something!'

'What can we do?' whimpered the tailor.

'Take the body in your arms,' she said. 'We will cover it with a shawl and carry it out of the house this very night. I will walk in front, crying, "My child is ill, my poor child is ill! Who can direct us to a doctor's house?"'

Encouraged by her plan, the tailor wrapped up the hunchback in a large silken shawl and carried him out into the street, his wife lamenting, 'My child! My child! Who will save him from the foul smallpox?'

So all who saw them whispered, 'They are carrying a child stricken with the smallpox.'

Thus they proceeded through the streets, inquiring for the doctor's house as they went, until at last they were directed to the house of a Jewish doctor. They knocked, and the door was opened by a slave girl.

'Give your master this piece of silver,' said the 23

tailor's wife, 'and beg him to come down and see my child; for he is very ill.'

As soon as the girl had gone in to call the doctor, the tailor's wife slipped into the doorway and said to her husband, 'Let us leave the hunchback here and run for our lives!'

The tailor propped up the body at the bottom of the staircase, and the pair made off as fast as their legs could carry them.

The Jew rejoiced on receiving the piece of silver. He rose quickly and, hurrying down the stairs in the dark, stumbled against the corpse and knocked it over. Terrified at the sight of the lifeless hunchback, and thinking that he himself had just caused his death, the Jew called on Moses and Aaron and Ezra and Joshua son of Nun, and reminded himself of the Ten Commandments, wringing his hands and crying, 'How will I get rid of the body?' Then he took up the hunchback and bore him to his wife and told her what had happened.

'You stand there doing nothing?' exclaimed the terrified woman. 'If the corpse remains here till daybreak we are lost! Come, we will carry the body up to the terrace and throw it into the courtyard of our neighbor the Moslem.'

Now, the Moslem was the steward of the royal kitchens, from which he seldom departed with his pockets empty. His house was always infested with rats and mice, which ate the butter, the cheese, and the wheat; and on fine nights the stray cats and dogs of the neighborhood came down and feasted on the contents of the kitchen. So the Jew and his wife, carrying the hunchback, climbed down from their terrace into their neighbor's courtyard and propped the hunchback up against the wall of the kitchen.

It was not long before the steward, who had been out all day, returned home. He opened the door and lit a candle – then started at the sight of a man leaning against the wall of his kitchen. 'So our thief is a man after all!' he thought; and, taking up a mallet, he cried, 'By Allah! to think it was you, and not the cats and dogs, who stole the meat and the butter! I have killed almost all the stray cats and dogs of the district and never thought of you and your like, who come prowling around the terraces.'

25

He knocked the hunchback down with the mallet and dealt him another blow on the chest as he lay on the ground. But the angry steward soon found that the man was dead. He was seized with fear, and exclaimed, 'There is no strength or power save in Allah! A curse upon the meat and the butter, and upon this night which has witnessed your death at my hands, you wretch!'

He lifted the hunchback onto his shoulders and left the house. The night was already nearing its end. The steward walked with his burden through the deserted streets until he entered a lane leading to the market place, and came to a shop that stood on a corner. There he leaned the hunchback up against the wall and hurried away.

Soon after, a Christian, who was the king's saddler, passed through the lane on his way to the public baths. He was fuddled with drink, and as he reeled along, he kept muttering to himself, 'Doomsday has come! The Last Judgment has come!' and staggering from one side of the lane to the other. Suddenly he bumped into the

26 hunchback.

Now, it so chanced that earlier in the evening the Christian had been robbed of his turban and was forced to buy another. So, on suddenly seeing this figure against the wall, he imagined, in his stupor, that it was someone who was about to snatch off his new turban and, taking the hunchback by the throat, felled him with a re-sounding blow. Then he raised a great outcry, screaming and cursing and calling out to the watchman of the market place.

The watchman arrived to find a Christian beating a Moslem.

'Get up and let go of him!' he shouted angrily. Then he found that the hunchback was dead. 'A fine state of affairs when a Christian dares to kill a Believer!' he exclaimed.

Confounded at the swift death of his victim, the Christian began to call on Jesus and Mary: thus, as the proverb has it, intoxication departed and meditation took its place. The watchman took hold of the Christian saddler, manacled him, and dragged him away to the governor's house.

In the morning the governor gave orders for

the hanging of the Christian. The town crier proclaimed his crime in the streets, and a gallows was set up in the heart of the city. Then came the executioner who, in the presence of the governor, stood the Christian beneath the gallows and put the rope around his neck.

At this moment the King's steward pushed his way through the crowd, crying, 'Do not hang him! It was I who killed the hunchback!'

'Why did you kill him?' asked the governor.

'It all happened,' replied the steward, 'when I returned home last night and found him in my house, about to break into the kitchen. I struck him with a mallet and he fell down dead upon the instant. In despair, I carried him to a lane adjoining the market place. Is it not enough to have killed a Moslem?' added the steward passionately. 'Must a Christian also die on my account? Therefore, hang no man but me!'

Hearing this, the governor set the Christian free and gave the executioner a fresh order. 'Hang the steward instead, on the grounds of his own confession.'

The executioner led the steward to the scaffold and had just placed the rope around his neck when the Jewish doctor forced his way through the crowd. 'Do not hang him!' he cried. 'I am the man who killed the hunchback!' And he told the governor his own version of the hunchback's death. 'Is my sin not great enough that I have killed a man unwittingly?' he added. 'Must another be killed through my crime, and with my knowledge?'

On hearing this, the governor gave orders that the Jew be hanged in place of the steward. But as the rope was being placed around his neck, the tailor came forward and cried, 'Do not hang him! No one killed the hunchback but myself!' And he related to the astonished assembly the true circumstances of the hunchback's death.

The governor marveled at the story and commented, 'This episode ought to be recorded in books.' And he ordered the executioner to set the Jew at liberty and to hang the tailor.

'Would to heaven they would make up their minds,' muttered the executioner, understandably impatient at the delay. 'The day will end before we hang any of them.' He resolutely placed the rope around the tailor's neck.

Now, the hunchback, the cause of all this commotion, was the King's jester and favorite companion. Finding that his jester had been absent from the royal palace all night and all the next morning, the monarch ordered his attendants to look for him. They soon returned to inform him of the hunchback's death and his self-confessed murderers.

'Go to the governor,' said the King to his chamberlain, 'and get him to bring them all before me.'

The chamberlain hurried at once to the city square, where the executioner was about to hang the tailor. 'Stop! Stop! Don't hang him!' he shouted, rushing through the crowd. And before the executioner could complete his work, the chamberlain informed the governor of the King's orders and took him to the royal palace, together with the tailor, the Christian, the Jew, the steward, and the hunchback's body.

When they had all been admitted to the King's presence, the governor kissed the ground before him and related all that had happened. The King marveled greatly and gave orders that the story be inscribed on parchment in letters of gold. Then he turned to those who were present and asked, 'Have you ever heard a tale more astonishing than this story of the hunchback?'

The tailor came forward, and said, 'Of all the tales of marvel that I have heard, Your Majesty, none surpasses in wonder an incident that I witnessed yesterday.

'Early in the morning, before I met the hunchback, I was at a breakfast party given by a friend to some twenty tradesmen and craftsmen of the city, among them tailors, drapers, carpenters, and others. As soon as the sun rose and the food was set before us, our host ushered into the room a handsome but noticeably lame young man, richly dressed in the Baghdad fashion. The young man greeted the company, and we all rose to receive him. But when he was about to sit down, he caught sight of one of the guests and, instead of taking his seat, made for the door. We all expressed surprise and concern, and our host held the young man by the arm and earnestly pleaded with him to explain his abrupt departure.

'"Sir," he answered, "do not try to detain me. If you must know, it is the presence of this obnoxious barber that compels me to leave at once."

'Our host was greatly astonished at these words, and the rest of us, too, wondered why the young man, a stranger in this city, should have taken offense at the barber's presence. We begged him to tell us the reason.

'"Gentlemen," he answered, "this barber was the cause of a grave disaster that befell me in Baghdad, my native city. Thanks to him my leg was broken and I am now lame. I have sworn never to sit in the same room with him, nor live in any town where he resides. This is why I left Baghdad, yet here I find him again. Not another night will I spend in this city."

'"By Allah," we said, "let us hear your story."

'The barber hung his head as the young man proceeded to tell of his adventure.'

The Tale of the Lame Young Man and the Barber of Baghdad

YOU should know that my father was one of the chief merchants of Baghdad and I was his only son. When I reached manhood my father died, leaving me great wealth and a numerous retinue of slaves and servants. From that time I began to live sumptuously, wearing the richest clothes and eating the choicest dishes. But I always avoided the company of women, for I felt shy and uneasy with them.

It so chanced, however, that one day, as I was walking along a narrow lane in Baghdad, a crowd of women barred my way. To get away from them I slipped into a quiet alleyway and sat down on a bench. I had not been there long when a window in the house opposite was flung open, and there appeared a young girl who was like the full moon in her beauty. She was watering the flowerpots on her window sill when, glancing around for the moment, she caught sight of me; whereupon she shut the window and disappeared. I fell in love with her at first sight and sat there forgetful of my surroundings until sunset, when the cadi of Baghdad came riding by, with slaves before him and servants behind him. Imagine my feelings, gentlemen, when I saw him dismount and enter the very house where the young girl lived; for I then realized that she was the cadi's daughter.

I returned home very sad at the thought that I would never be able to make her acquaintance. Presently, however, there entered my room an old woman of my household, who at once understood the cause of my sadness. She sat at my bedside and comforted me, saying, 'Tell me everything, my son, and let me be your messenger.'

When she had heard my story she said, 'You must know that this girl lives with her father, the cadi, in the strictest seclusion. But I am a frequent visitor to their house, and I will undertake to bring you together. Do not despair. I will go there at once.'

I was greatly consoled by her words. The old woman departed on her errand but soon returned crestfallen.

'My son,' she said, 'do not ask the outcome of my visit. Scarcely had I begun to speak of you when the girl cried, "Hold your tongue, old woman, or you will receive the punishment you deserve."'

Seeing that this news had dashed my spirits, the old woman added, 'Do not fear – I will shortly approach her again.'

My grief was almost too deep to bear until, after a few days, the woman came again and said, 'Rejoice, I bring you good news! Yesterday I visited the girl again. When she saw me in tears and asked me the reason for my weeping, I replied, "I have come from a young man who is languishing with love for you." Her heart was moved, and she asked, "Who may he be?" "He is the flower of my life," I answered, "and as dear to me as my own son. Some days ago he saw you at your window, watering your flowers. He loved you from that moment. But when I told him of your harsh response after I mentioned him to you, he began to pine away and took to his bed, where he now lies dying." "And all this on account of me?" asked the girl, moved with pity and love. "Yes, by Allah," I replied. "Go back to him," she said. "Give him my greetings and say that my love is as great as his. Ask him to come and see me on Friday next, before the midday prayers. I will let him into the house myself. But he must leave before my father returns from the mosque."'

This report filled me with joy and I handsomely rewarded the old woman for her labors. My grief completely left me, and my household rejoiced at my recovery.

When Friday came, I made ready for the great occasion, putting on my finest robes and sweetest perfumes, and then sat waiting for the hour of midday prayers. But the old woman hinted that a visit from the barber might do much to improve my appearance. I called my slave and said to him, 'Go to the market place and bring me a barber. See that he is a man of sense who will attend to his business and will not annoy me with idle chatter.' The slave went away and brought back with him a barber who was none other than the odious old man you see before you.

36   As soon as he arrived, the barber said that I

looked very pale; and when I explained that I had but recently recovered from an illness, he congratulated me, saying, 'May Allah preserve you, sir, from all misfortune, all distress, all grief, and all sorrow!'

'Allah grant your prayer!' I replied.

'Now tell me, sir,' he said, 'do you wish to have your head shaved? You doubtless know that the famous Ibn Abbas (may Allah rest his soul in peace!) has said, "He who has his head shaved on a Friday will ward off seventy calamities."'

'Enough of this talk, old man!' I cried. 'Come now, begin shaving my head at once.'

He produced from his pocket a large bundle. Imagine my astonishment when I saw him take from it, not a razor or a pair of scissors as one might have expected, but an astrological device made of seven plates of polished silver. He carried it to the middle of the courtyard, and, raising the instrument toward the sun, gazed intently at the reflection for a long time. Then he came back to me and said solemnly, 'Know that of this day, Friday the tenth of the second month of the year two hundred and fifty-three after the Flight of the Prophet (upon whom be Allah's blessing and peace), and twelve hundred and thirty-one in the year of Alexander the Great, there have elapsed eight degrees and six minutes; and that, according to the strictest rules of computation, the planet Mars, in conjunction with Mercury, is this day in the ascendant: all this denoting an excellent moment for haircutting. Furthermore, my instrument clearly informs me that it is your intention to pay a visit to a certain person, and that of this nothing shall come but evil. There is also another sign in connection with a certain matter, of which I would rather not speak.'

'By Allah!' I cried, 'this is intolerable! You weary me with your tedious chatter, and, what is more, your forebodings are far from encouraging. I sent for you to shave my head. Do so at once and cease your babbling!'

'If only you knew the gravity of the impending disaster,' he said, 'you would listen to my advice and heed the warning of the stars!'

'Doubtless,' I cried, 'you are the only astrologer among the barbers of Baghdad: but, allow me to tell you, old man, you are also an impudent mischief-maker and a frivolous chatterbox.'

'What would you have?' cried he, shrugging his shoulders. 'Allah has sent you one who is not only a barber of great repute, but also a master of the arts and sciences: one who is not only deeply versed in alchemy, astrology, mathematics, and architecture, but also (to mention only a few of my accomplishments) well taught in the arts of logic, rhetoric, and elocution. Add to all this the maturity of judgment that can be acquired only through long experience of the world. Your late father, young man, loved me for my wisdom; and it is the memory of his goodness and kind favors that prompts me to render you an honest service. Far from being a meddlesome gossip, as you seem to suggest, I am, in fact, well known for my gravity and reserve; on account of which qualities people call me 'the Silent One.' Instead of crossing and thwarting me, young man, it would be much more befitting to thank Allah for my sound advice and my concern for your well-being. Would that I were a whole year in your service, that you might learn to do me justice!'

Here I exclaimed, 'You will surely be my death this day!' But when the old man was about to resume his talk, I felt as though I were about to explode with rage, so I said to my slave, 'In Allah's name, give this man a silver piece and show him out, for I do not wish to have my head shaved after all.'

'What kind of talk is this?' cried the barber. 'By Allah, I will accept nothing before I have shaved you. You must know that I would regard it as a pleasant duty and a great honor to serve you even without payment. For although you do not seem to appreciate my merits, I appreciate yours. I remember one Friday when I was sent for by your late father (may Allah have mercy upon him: he was a man of rare qualities). I found him entertaining a company of visitors. He welcomed me as he might have welcomed an old friend, and said, 'I beg you to cut my hair.' At once I took out my astrolabe, computed the

height of the sun, and soon ascertained that the

hour was clearly unfavorable for haircutting. I did not hesitate to tell him the truth. He accepted my judgment and readily agreed to wait for a good moment. Incidentally, it might interest you to know that, while we waited, I composed half a dozen verses in his praise and recited them before the company. Your father was so pleased with them that he ordered his slave to give me a hundred and three dinars and a robe of honor. When the awaited hour had come and I had cut his hair, I asked him in a whisper, "Why did you pay me a hundred and three dinars?" "One dinar is for your wisdom," he replied, "one for the hair-cutting, and one for the pleasure of your company; as for the remainder and the robe of honor, pray accept them as a slight reward for your excellent poem." '

'Then may Allah have mercy on my father,' I burst out, 'if he ever had dealings with a barber like you!'

'There is no god but Allah, and Mohammed is his Prophet!' exclaimed the barber, laughing and shaking his head. 'Glory to him who changes others and remains himself unchanged! I always took you for a sensible and intelligent young man: now I see that your illness has slightly affected your head. You would do well to remember that Allah in his Sacred Book mentioned with special praise those who curb their anger and forgive their fellow men. I will forgive you.

'As I was saying, neither your father nor your grandfather before him ever did anything without first seeking my advice. You have doubtless heard the proverb "He who takes good counsel is crowned with success." Now, you will find no one better versed in the ways of the world than myself; and here I stand, waiting to serve you. What I cannot understand, however, is that you seem to be a little tired of me, when I am not in the least tired of you. But the high esteem in which I hold your father's memory will always make me mindful of my duty to his son.'

'By Allah,' I yelled, 'this has gone too far!' I was about to order my slaves to throw him out of the house when he suddenly began to dampen my hair, and before I knew what was happening my head was covered with lather.

'I will take no offense, sir,' continued the wretched old man, quite unruffled, 'if you are a little short-tempered. Apart from the strain of your recent illness, you are, of course, very young. It seems but yesterday that I used to carry you to school on my shoulders.'

Unable to contain myself any longer, I said solemnly, 'My friend, I must beg you to get on with your work.'

'And have I, sir, all this time, been engaged in anything else?' was his reply.

Here I tore my clothes and began to shriek like a madman.

When he saw me do this, the barber calmly produced a razor and began to strop it, passing it up and down the piece of leather with deadly deliberation. At length, he held my head with one hand and shaved off a few hairs. Then he raised his hand and said, 'I do not suppose you are aware of my standing in society. These hands of mine have dressed the heads of kings and princes, viziers and noblemen. Have you not heard the poet's verses in my praise?'

At this point I interrupted him again. 'You have stifled me with your nonsense!'

'It has just occurred to me that you might be in a hurry,' said the barber.

'I am,' I shouted, 'I am!'

'Well, well,' he went on, 'haste is a bad thing and leads only to ruin and repentance. The Prophet said: "The best enterprises are those that are carried out with caution." I wish you would tell me the purpose of your haste, as there are yet quite three hours to midday prayers.' Here the barber paused, and then added, 'But let me first make sure of the correct time.'

So saying, he flung away the razor, took up the astrolabe, and went out into the courtyard. There he observed the sun for a long time, and at last came back, saying, 'It is now three hours to midday prayers, neither one minute more nor one minute less.'

'For Allah's sake,' I cried, 'hold your tongue! You have goaded me beyond endurance.'

Again he took up the razor and proceeded to strop it as he had done before. Scarcely had he removed a few hairs when he again stopped and said, 'I am rather anxious about you, you know. It would be in your own interest to tell me the cause of your haste. For, as you know, your father and grandfather never did anything without consulting me.'

I realized that I should never be able to evade his persistent questioning. To cut the matter short, I said that I had been invited to a party at the house of a friend and begged him to stop being impertinent.

At the mention of a party the barber exclaimed, 'This reminds me that I myself am expecting a few friends at my house today. But I have forgotten to provide anything for them to eat. Think of the disgrace!'

'Do not be troubled over this matter,' I replied. 'All the food and drink in my house is yours if you will only finish shaving my head.'

'Sir,' he cried, 'may Allah reward you for your generosity! Pray let me hear what you have for my guests.'

'Five different meat dishes,' I answered, 'ten stuffed chickens finely broiled, and a roasted lamb!'

'Be so good,' he said, 'as to let me look at them.'

I ordered the provisions to be brought before him, together with a cask of wine.

'How generous you are!' he exclaimed. 'But what shall we do without incense and perfume?'

I ordered my slave to set before him a box containing aloeswood, musk, and ambergris, the whole worth not less than fifty gold pieces. Time was running short, so I said, 'All this is yours; only, for the sake of Mohammed, on whom be Allah's blessing and peace, finish shaving my head!'

'Pray allow me to see the contents of the box,' he replied.

My slave opened it, and the barber put aside his razor and sat down on the floor, examining the incense. He then rose and, taking up his razor again, held my head and shaved off a few more hairs.

'My son,' he said, with great satisfaction, 'I do not know how to thank you. The party I am giving today will now owe a great deal to your

kindness. Although none of my guests might be

considered worthy of such magnificence, they are all quite respectable. First, there is Zantoot, the bathkeeper; then Salee'a, the corn merchant; Akrasha, the fruit seller; Hamid, the trash collector; Silat, the grocer; Abu Makarish, the milkman; Kaseem, the watchman; and last, but by no means least, Sa'eed, the camel driver. Each one of them is a delightful companion and has a song and dance of his own invention; and is, like your humble servant, neither inquisitive nor given to idle talk. In truth, no description of my friends can do them justice. If, therefore, you would care to honor us with your company, you will have a more pleasant time, and we will all be the happier. In my opinion, one reason why you would do well not to visit those friends of yours is the possibility of meeting some busybody who will split your head with incessant chatter.'

I choked with rage, and burst into a fit of hysterical laughter, but calmed down sufficiently to say, 'I should be delighted to come some other time. Shave my head now and let me go my way. Besides, your friends must be waiting for you.'

'But how I long to introduce you to these excellent fellows!' he continued. 'Once you meet them, you will give up all your friends forever.'

'May Allah give you joy in them,' I said. 'I shall doubtless have the pleasure of meeting them one day.'

'Well, well,' he went on, shrugging his shoulders, 'if you must go to your friends, I will now carry to my guests the presents with which you have favored me. As I do not stand upon ceremony with them I will return without delay to accompany you to your party.'

Here I lost all control of myself and cried, 'There is no strength or help save in Allah! Pray go to your friends and delight your heart with them, and let me go to mine; for they are waiting for me.'

But the barber cried, 'I will not let you go alone.'

'The truth is,' I said, 'that no one may be admitted to the house where I am going except myself.'

'Aha!' he exclaimed. 'It must be a woman,

then, or else you would allow me to accompany you. Yet I am the right man for that kind of adventure and could do much in an emergency. Why, you may even get yourself murdered! Furthermore, you know how ruthless the governor is about such secret meetings, particularly on a Friday.'

'Vile old man,' I cried, 'how can you speak so to my face?'

'Did you imagine,' retorted the barber, 'that you could hide such a design from me? My only concern, young man, is to serve you.'

Afraid that my servants might hear the barber's remarks, I made no answer.

The hour of prayer had come and the imams had already begun their sermons, when at long last the barber finished shaving my head.

'Take away this food to your house,' I said, 'and when you return we will go together to the party.'

But he would not believe my words. 'You want to get rid of me and go alone,' he replied. 'Think of the trap that may have been set for you! By Allah, you shall not leave the house 49 until I come back to accompany you and watch over your safety.'

'Very well,' I said, 'but you must not be late.'

The barber took all the meat and drink I had given him and left me in peace. But if you think the wretch carried the things home, you are wrong. He hired a porter for the task and hid himself in one of the neighboring alleyways.

The muezzins had now intoned their blessings on the Prophet from the minarets of the city. I rose quickly, flung on my cloak, and ran as fast as I could to the girl's house. Finding the door open, I hurried up the stairs to her apartment. But I had scarcely reached the second story when the cadi arrived. Seized by a great fear, I rushed to one of the windows overlooking the alleyway, and was confounded to see the barber (Allah's curse be upon him!) sitting on the doorstep.

Now, it so happened that immediately on his return from the mosque the cadi took it into his head to beat one of his maidservants. She raised

an uproar of wailing and screaming. A slave went

to her aid, but the furious cadi fell upon him also, and he joined in yelling for help.

Imagining that it was I who was the victim, the barber set up a great outcry in the street, tearing his clothes and scattering dust upon his head. 'Help! Help!' he cried. 'My master is being murdered by the cadi!'

Then, running frantically to my house with a great crowd following him, he roused my people and my servants; and before I knew what was happening they all came, men and women, to the cadi's house, with torn clothes and loosed tresses, lamenting, 'Alas! Our master is dead!'

The clamor in the street was heard by the cadi, who ordered a slave to find out what had happened. The slave quickly returned saying, 'There is a great multitude of men and women at the door. They are all shaking their fists and shouting, "Our master has been murdered!"'

The cadi rose in anger and opened the door to find an infuriated mob shouting threats at him.

'What is the meaning of this?' he demanded indignantly.

'Dog! Pig! Murderer!' shouted my servants. 'Where is our master?'

'What has your master done to me,' asked the cadi, 'that I should kill him?'

'You have just been flogging him,' replied the barber. 'I myself heard his cries.'

'But what has your master done that I should flog him?' repeated the cadi. 'And who brought him to my house?'

'Wicked old liar,' answered the barber, 'do not pretend to be so innocent, for I know the whole truth and every detail of the matter. Your daughter is in love with him and he with her. When you caught him in the house you ordered your slaves to flog him. By Allah, the Caliph himself shall judge this outrage! Give us back our master, or else I will have to enter by force and rescue him myself.'

Embarrassed and perplexed, the cadi said, 'If you are not lying, come and bring him out.'

I saw the barber push his way through the door. I desperately looked for a means of escape, but could find none. At length I saw in one of the rooms an empty wooden chest into which I jumped and pulled down the lid. But there was no escape from the barber. He came running into the room, looked right and left, and instantly guessed where I was. He was a stronger man than I thought, for he hoisted the chest onto his shoulder and carried it down the stairs. But as he rushed through the door, he tripped over the threshold, hurling me out of the chest into the crowded street. My leg was broken, but my single thought at that moment was to fly for my life. I took from my pockets handfuls of gold and threw them to the crowd. While they were busy scrambling for the coins I made off, hobbling through the back streets as fast as I could manage.

The barber pursued me, crying, 'The blackguards would have killed my master! Praise be to Allah who aided me against them and saved my master from their hands!'

Then, calling out to me as he ran, he continued, 'Now you see the fruits of your rashness and impatience! Had not Allah sent me to your rescue, you would not have escaped alive today. I have risked my life in your service; but you would not even hear of taking me with you. All the same, I will not be angry, for you are very young and exceedingly rash and foolish.'

Writhing with the pain in my leg and the anguish in my heart, I turned on my heel and threw these words at the jabbering monster: 'Is it not enough that you have brought me to this pass? Must you also hound me to my death in the middle of the market place?' Then, quickly entering a weaver's shop, I begged asylum of him and implored him to drive the barber away.

I sat in the back room prostrated with fear. I thought, 'If I return home, I will never be able to rid myself of this fiend.' I felt certain he would pursue me like a shadow, and I could endure the sight of him no longer.

I sent out for witnesses and wrote my will, dividing my property among my people. I appointed a guardian over them, and committed to him the charge of the young and the aged, and also the sale of my house and other estates. I then left Baghdad and came to live in your city, imagining that I had forever freed myself from this man. Yet no sooner had I stepped into this house than I found him sitting among you as an honored guest. How can my heart be at rest or my stay be pleasant when I am under the same roof as the man who did all this to me and was the cause of my lameness?

The young man (continued the tailor) refused to sit down and went away. When we had heard his story, we turned to the barber and asked, 'Is it true what this young man has said of you?'

'By Allah, gentlemen,' replied the barber, 'I must assure you that had it not been for my presence of mind, resourcefulness, and personal courage, this youth would have surely died. He should, indeed, be thankful that his folly cost him merely his leg, and not his life. This young man has accused me of being talkative and meddlesome – two vices from which, unlike my six brothers, I am entirely free. To prove to you the falseness of this charge, however, I will now tell you a story, and you shall judge for your-selves that I am a man not only of few words but also of great generosity and chivalry.'

The Barber's Tale

THE little adventure I am about to relate happened to me some years ago during the reign of our former Caliph. (May Allah have mercy upon him: he was a just ruler and a righteous man.)

One day I came across a group of ten men whom (as I discovered later) the Caliph wished to punish as rogues. He ordered his lieutenant to bring them before him. It so chanced that just as they were being taken onto a boat to cross the river Tigris I was taking the air along the riverbank. Drawing close to them, I thought to myself, 'This must be a pleasure party. They will probably spend the day in this boat eating and drinking. By Allah, I will be their guest and make merry with them.'

I jumped into the boat and sat in their midst. But as soon as we set foot on the opposite bank, the governor's guards took hold of us and put chains around the necks of the men, and around my neck also. However, I uttered not a syllable (which, I submit, is but a proof of my courage and discretion). Then they dragged us away to the Caliph's court and led us before the Commander of the Faithful.

When he saw us, the Caliph called the executioner and said to him, 'Strike off the heads of these ten wretches!'

The executioner made us kneel down in a row before the Caliph; then he unsheathed his sword and beheaded the unfortunate men.

Seeing me kneeling still at the end of the row, the Caliph cried, 'Why did you not kill the tenth man?'

The executioner counted aloud the ten heads and the ten bodies that lay on the ground – and the Caliph turned to me and said, 'Who are you, and how did you come to be among these criminals?'

Then, and only then, did I decide to break my silence.

'Commander of the Faithful,' I replied, 'I am called the Silent One and my wisdom is proverbial. I am a barber by trade and one of the seven sons of my father.' I then explained how I was 57 mistaken for one of the prisoners and briefly outlined my life's history.

When he was satisfied that I was a man of rare qualities, the Caliph smiled, saying, 'Tell me, noble sheikh, are your six brothers like you, distinguished for their deep learning and the brevity of their speeches?'

'Gracious heavens!' I replied. 'Each of them is such a disreputable good-for-nothing that you almost slander me by comparing me to them. Because of their recklessness, stupidity, and unusual cowardice, they have brought upon themselves all kinds of misfortunes and bodily deformities: the first is lame, the second loose-limbed and disfigured, the third blind, the fourth one-eyed, and the fifth ear-cropped, and the sixth has had both his lips cut off. Were it not for the fear that you might take me for an idle gossip, I would gladly tell you their stories.'

Thereupon the Commander of the Faithful gave me leave to relate to him the story of my first brother.

PENGUIN CHILDREN'S 60s

Some other Puffin books retold by N. J. Dawood

ALADDIN AND OTHER TALES FROM THE
ARABIAN NIGHTS
SINDBAD THE SAILOR AND OTHER TALES
FROM THE ARABIAN NIGHTS